THIS BOOK BELONGS TO:

☐ Witch   ☐ Wizard

☐ Muggle/No-Maj   ☐ Squib

FANTASTIC BEASTS

A CINEMATIC YEARBOOK

IMAGINE ◆ DRAW ◆ CREATE

CONTENTS

A WIZARD RETURNS

Newt Scamander's mission is to find and study rare and endangered magical creatures around the world.

His book, *Fantastic Beasts and Where to Find Them*, aims to educate the magical community about the beauty and wonder of these beasts, in the hope that these extraordinary species will one day be able to live in harmony with witches and wizards. Magical creatures are not to be feared!

When Newt arrived in New York City, having travelled the world studying his creatures, his stay there was supposed to be brief. However, when his magical case was switched with one belonging to a No-Maj, it led to the escape of some of Newt's fantastic beasts!

Troubling times were ahead as sinister forces threatened the city and risked exposing the underground magical community forever. Newt became an unlikely hero and helped to capture a Dark wizard.

Now, with the Obscurus supposedly destroyed and Gellert Grindelwald behind bars, what does the future hold for the wizarding world? Read on to join Newt and his friends in their fantastic adventures and witness their struggle against Dark magic.

TRAVELLING LIGHT

Meet Newt Scamander, a Magizoologist and wizard who travels the world studying and rescuing magical creatures. His only luggage is a single battered case.

Newt arrives in the United States in 1926 to complete a special task – he must safely return one of his beasts, Frank the Thunderbird, to his home in Arizona. Is this the only reason for his New York stopover, or is something else drawing him to the city?

A Thunderbird is a large, flying beast. Its multiple powerful wings shimmer with cloud- and sun-like patterns and their flapping can create storms.

SURPRISING SHED

Newt's ordinary-looking case expands into an astonishing world of magical creatures. Newt's shed is where he keeps his notebooks, potions and plants. Imagine you had your own magical shed filled with various potions and plants. Draw some of your own magical items in the jars below.

NEWT SCAMANDER'S JOURNAL

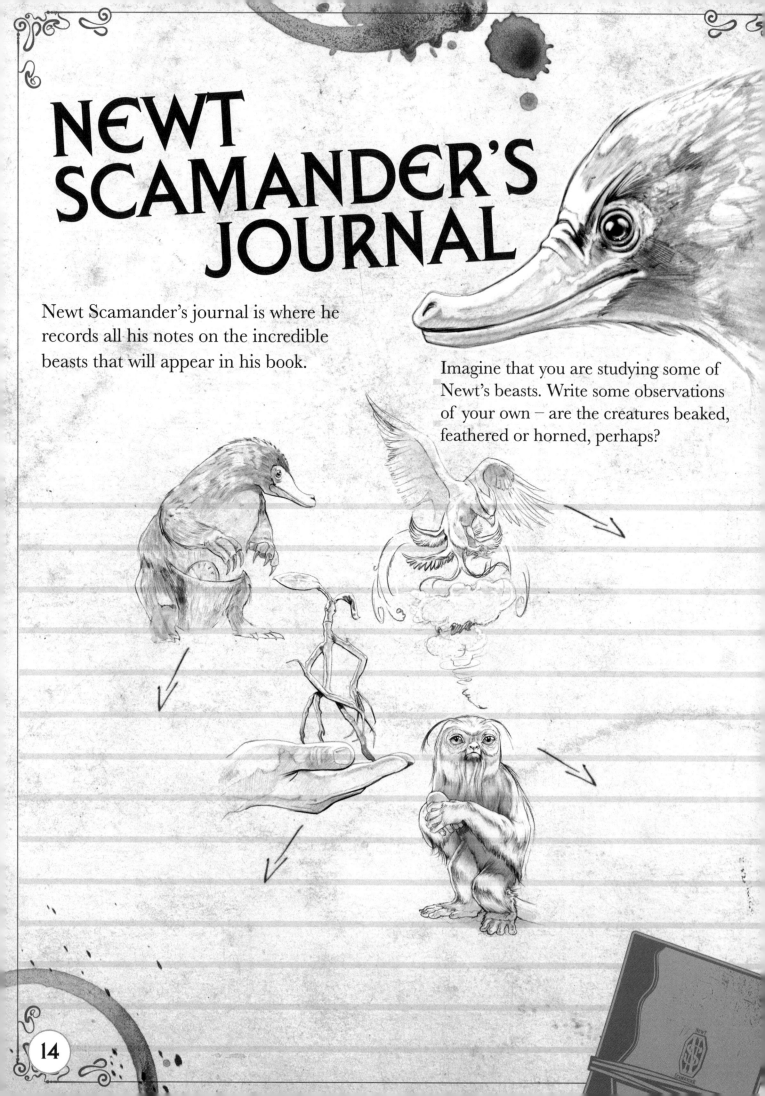

Newt Scamander's journal is where he records all his notes on the incredible beasts that will appear in his book.

Imagine that you are studying some of Newt's beasts. Write some observations of your own – are the creatures beaked, feathered or horned, perhaps?

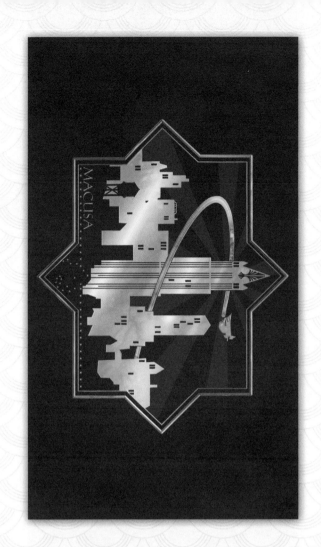

STOP, THIEF!

Nifflers are known for their love of shiny objects. What does this thief have his eye on next? Draw a sparkling treasure you could imagine finding in the pickpocket's pouch.

ON THE LOOSE

When Jacob accidentally releases the beasts from Newt's case, the creatures roam free all over New York! Each beast was recaptured in different locations in the city.

JACOB'S APARTMENT
CREATURE: *Murtlap*

Jacob receives an unexpected surprise when he opens what he thinks is his case in his tiny apartment – along with a beastly bite!

CENTRAL PARK ZOO
CREATURE: *Erumpent*

This horned beast charges to the famous zoo in Central Park, Manhattan, in search of a mate.

FANCY DEPARTMENT STORE
CREATURE: *Occamy*

A newly hatched creature with plumes and a serpentine body is hiding in a large department store. Newt has to use a teapot to trap the huge creature, which has grown to fit its space.

DIAMOND DISTRICT JEWELLER'S SHOP
CREATURE: *Niffler*

This bothersome burrower makes a smash and grab in New York's Diamond District, landing Newt and Jacob in trouble with the police.

Think about where your favourite hiding place is. Write about it below.

_____

_____

_____

_____

_____

_____

Pickett the Bowtruckle doesn't go missing like Newt's other beasts. He likes to hide in the top pocket of Newt's coat.

NOTHING IS AS IT SEEMS

On his arrival in the Big Apple, Newt had to quickly decide whom he could trust – not everyone is as they first appear. What do you think?

Tick the people you think are honest and put a cross next to those you're not sure can be trusted.

PERCIVAL GRAVES, DIRECTOR OF MAGICAL SECURITY AT MACUSA

Graves is a highly respected MACUSA official, but spends a lot of time with Credence Barebone, hiding a Deathly Hallows necklace around his neck.

MARY LOU BAREBONE, NEW SALEM PHILANTHROPIC SOCIETY (NSPS) LEADER

Mary Lou offers food and shelter to the city's orphans, though not without a catch.

TINA GOLDSTEIN, MACUSA OFFICE WORKER

Once an excellent Auror at the Ministry, Tina was demoted after she refused to follow orders. She gets close to Newt, but this doesn't stop her handing him over to the Ministry.

CREDENCE BAREBONE, ADOPTED SON OF MARY LOU

Credence has close connections with Percival Graves, but hides a dark secret.

JACOB KOWALSKI, CANNING FACTORY WORKER

Jacob seeks a loan to open his own bakery and first meets Newt at the City Bank. As a No-Maj, is he putting the magical community at risk?

SERAPHINA PICQUERY, MACUSA PRESIDENT

The President's goal is to keep the magical community in the USA safe, which means keeping it completely secret from No-Majs – at any cost.

QUEENIE GOLDSTEIN, MACUSA WAND PERMIT OFFICER

A witch best known for her beauty, Queenie proves there's more to her than meets the eye, as she possesses a special power – she can read minds.

HENRY SHAW SR, NEWSPAPER MAGNATE

Henry is a powerful media mogul. His newspapers give him the opportunity to influence millions of No-Maj readers.

MODESTY BAREBONE, ADOPTED DAUGHTER OF MARY LOU

Modesty does everything she is told by her adoptive mother, but is fascinated by magic – which is forbidden in the Barebone household.

GNARLAK, GOBLIN OWNER OF THE BLIND PIG

A gangster goblin, who is only willing to exchange information if there's something in it for himself.

CITY IN CHAOS

Newt arrives in New York at a time when the city is on high alert. A mysterious magical force is leaving a path of destruction – crushing cars, blasting through walls and shattering windows. Once MACUSA learns about Newt's escaped creatures, the beasts become prime suspects.

A Dark presence is terrorizing the city.

The sinister events make headline news in the city's magical newspaper.

ENCHANTED DISPATCHES TO THE AMERICAN WIZARD

THE NEW YORK GHOST

VOL. LXIII · NO. 190871 · DAILY

MONDAY 6TH DECEMBER 1926

PRICE 0.05 DRAGOTS

★ SUNSET FINAL EDITION ★ · WEATHER · BOOK OF THE WEEK: The Flap of the Cape · WEST COAST SUPPLEMENT EVERY THURSDAY · RECRUITMENT · Pg 3 · POTIONS · Pg 6 · SPELLS · Pg 8 · INTERNATIONAL · Pg 8 · LITTLE WIZARDS · Pg 9 · THE NEW YORK GHOST SUBSCRIPTION

MAGICAL DISTURBANCES RISK WIZARDING EXPOSURE

THE MACUSA INDEX OF MAGICAL EXPOSURE THREAT – No.50.26

PRESIDENT SERAPHINA PICQUERY TO ADDRESS FEARFUL AMERICAN WIZARDING COMMUNITY

MACUSA ON MAXIMUM ALERT - FULL REPORT PG.13

• International Confederation of Wizards called for emergency meeting. Pgs 15/17

Thousands of letters will be dispatched across America from tomorrow. Owls on stand by.

CULTURE

WIZZ JAZZ TAKES NEW YORK BY STORM

"Big Foot Last Stand" gets Wizard Broadway adaptation

SPORTS

WIZARDS INTRIGUED YET FASCINATED BY NO-MAJ BASEBALL

GELLERT GRINDELWALD INTERNATIONAL WIZARD HUNT INTENSIFIES

Fitchburg Finches scores high at the USA Quidditch League

Suspicious Wizards questioned by MACUSA officials

What is this

EMERGENCY
LEVEL 6

SEVERE: UNEXPLAINED ACTIVITY

DANGER
LEVEL 4

HIGH ALERT
LEVEL 3

MODERATE THREAT
LEVEL 2

LOW THREAT
LEVEL 1

ZERO THREAT

WITCH HUNTS
EXPOSURES
OBLIVIATIONS

537
082
910

No-Maj Mary Lou Barebone is the leader of the New Salem Philanthropic Society. She believes that witchcraft and wizardry is at play, and will stop at nothing to get her message heard.

The MACUSA Magical Exposure Threat Level clock, showing the threat level to the wizarding community, reads as 'severe'.

NO WITCHCRAFT IN AMERICA!
WE NEED A SECOND SALEM

We march for America and for Justice!

FANTASTIC
BEASTS

Newt must track down every one of his runaway beasts … and fast!

Although no longer a MACUSA Auror, Tina Goldstein keeps Newt under close surveillance.

WIZARDING WORK

Newt and his friends do very different jobs – from important roles at the Ministry to a baker of treats for the No-Maj community. Which of their jobs could you imagine doing?

TINA GOLDSTEIN

AUROR, MACUSA INVESTIGATIVE TEAM

Tina was allowed to return to her job as a highly trained Auror for MACUSA after helping to capture Grindelwald.

SKILLS:
Surveillance, a high level of intelligence, loyalty to MACUSA.

JACOB KOWALSKI

BAKER OF POLISH PASTRIES AND OTHER DELIGHTS

When a stranger gives him a case full of silver Occamy eggs, Jacob is able to open the Kowalski Bakery at last.

SKILLS:
Creativity, a love of baked goods, expert tastebuds.

QUEENIE GOLDSTEIN

WAND PERMIT OFFICER AT MACUSA

Queenie's talents as a Legilimens, dressmaker and cook are wasted at MACUSA, where she has an unexciting desk job.

SKILLS:
Filing, typing, patience.

SERAPHINA PICQUERY

MACUSA PRESIDENT

A strong and natural leader, Seraphina's priority at MACUSA is to keep the wizarding community secret. If witches and wizards were to be exposed to No-Majs, the results would be explosive.

SKILLS:
Decision-making, leadership, courage.

NEWT SCAMANDER

MAGIZOOLOGIST AND AUTHOR

Newt travels the world, studying and caring for magical creatures. He hopes that his book will educate the wizarding community on just how important it is to protect these beasts.

SKILLS:
A passion for magical creatures, medicine making, a love of travel.

Choose the role that you think would best suit you or come up with something of your own. Then write down your skills and draw yourself dressed for duty!

My wizarding work: _____

My skills: _____

_____

WORLDS APART

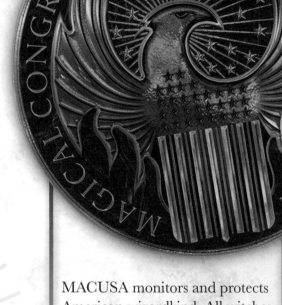

New York is a bustling city where witches and wizards share the streets with non-magical people, or No-Majs. While MACUSA does everything possible to keep its magical community underground, the New Salem Philanthropic Society (NSPS) warns of dangerous witches and wizards living in the city.

MACUSA monitors and protects American wizardkind. All witches and wizards must abide by MACUSA's laws that are designed to keep them safe.

Known as Muggles in the UK, non-magical people are named No-Majs in the United States.

Credence, Chastity and Modesty Barebone help spread their adoptive mother's message and rally other children to join the NSPS.

WITCHES LIVE AMONG US!

The NSPS puts up posters designed to scare people into joining their cause.

CASTING SPELLS

These fantastic spells all proved to be highly effective during Newt's New York adventures. Place a tick next to your favourite magical moment.

Incantation:	Reason cast:	By:	
Alohomora!	To open the bank vault and chase a Niffler.		☐
Finestra!	To shatter a glass window when trying to capture a Niffler.		☐
Accio!	To seize Graves' wand.		☐
Revelio!	To force Percival Graves to reveal his true identity.		☐
Aberto!	To try and open Graves' office		☐

Imagine a time that you might cast one of these spells. When might you use it?

_____

_____

_____

_____

IMPRISONED

When Newt and Tina are arrested for their suspected roles in the magical destruction of New York City, Percival Graves immediately sentences the pair without a trial.

Graves puts Newt behind bars and tells him to await his fate.

Tina is led away by MACUSA guards to an underground cell.

Newt makes his escape.

Queenie has an ambitious plan to save Newt, Tina and Jacob – she orders them to climb into Newt's case!

Tina must take a leap of faith by jumping onto the back of the Swooping Evil to safety. Newt releases the Swooping Evil again to stop the MACUSA guards in their tracks.

Pickett the Bowtruckle helps Newt escape by picking the lock on his handcuffs. Draw and colour Pickett in the grid below. Try copying the picture section by section.

SUBWAY BATTLE

Events come to a head in the City Hall subway station, when the Obscurus is destroyed and Percival Graves' true identity is exposed. The battle in the subway is a dark day in wizarding history.

Graves unleashes a powerful attack on his fellow Aurors.

Graves marvels at the power of the Obscurus

NEWT'S
MENAGERIE

CREATE A CREATURE

Imagine you had discovered a rare new magical species.
Tick the boxes to classify your beast, then draw what
it might look like below.

Is your beast...

Beaked (excl. Griffin)	
Feathered	
Horned	
Hooved (not Nogtails)	
Carapaced	

What is your beast's natural habitat?

Aquatic / Amphibious	
Burrowing	
Desert	
Tropical/Equatorial	
Temperate	

MINISTRATION CHART

Newt's detailed Ministration Chart allows him to keep track of the beasts in his care. The special feed codes and habitat and terrain codes remind him to create the perfect conditions for his creatures, as though they were living in their natural habitats.

Newt hopes to educate witches and wizards on how they can live in harmony with magical beasts, rather than fear them.

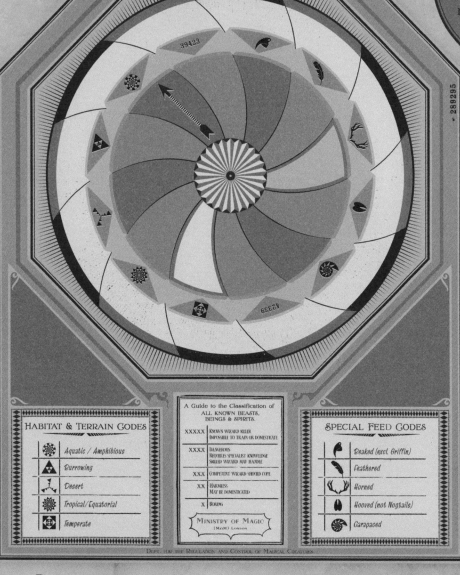

MINISTRATION CHART
To Assist Magical Creature Welfare and Development

HABITAT & TERRAIN CODES

✳	Aquatic / Amphibious
▲	Burrowing
⊥	Desert
✵	Tropical/Equatorial
◈	Temperate

A Guide to the Classification of ALL KNOWN BEASTS, BEINGS & SPIRITS.

XXXXX	KNOWN WIZARD KILLER IMPOSSIBLE TO TRAIN OR DOMESTICATE
XXXX	DANGEROUS REQUIRES SPECIALIST KNOWLEDGE SKILLED WIZARD MAY HANDLE
XXX	COMPETENT WIZARD SHOULD COPE
XX	HARMLESS MAY BE DOMESTICATED
X	BORING

MINISTRY OF MAGIC
[MoM] London

SPECIAL FEED CODES

◣	Beaked (excl. Griffin)
🪶	Feathered
🦌	Horned
⸙	Hooved (not Nogtails)
🐚	Carapaced

DEPT. FOR THE REGULATION AND CONTROL OF MAGICAL CREATURES

Beasts were once classified by the Ministry of Magic according to how dangerous a species they were.

Newt's assistant, Bunty, loves caring for magical creatures almost as much as Newt does!

BELOW GROUND

In the basement of his London residence, Newt has created an enormous menagerie and beast hospital. Here, he cares for endangered and injured creatures and loves each species equally.

POTION
Pus de
Bobotuber

Origine naturelle

Newt's Augurey is an owl-like bird with greenish-black plumage and a sharp, pointed beak.

The Niffler that travelled to New York with Newt now has four babies – each one with a craving for gold and silver!

NEW YORK

POINTED AS AUROR

BOLD BEASTS

Firedrakes are small dragon-like creatures with leathery wings. A Firedrake can create fire from the tip of its tail, causing deadly destruction.

Among the beasts in Newt's basement is the Kelpie, an underwater creature with equine features and long seaweed-like tendrils.

Colour in the rest of this majestic creature.

The Zouwu is a monstrously large feline beast – as big as an elephant – with a striped body, scraggly mane, four fangs that curl up out of its mouth and long, sharp claws. It has a distinctive multi-coloured tail.

Now draw your

MAGICAL MEDICINE

Don't forget to add a label!

NEW REMEDY

Imagine if you had Newt's skills of healing poorly creatures. What fantastic remedy would you make? Fill in the details below to write about your magical remedy.

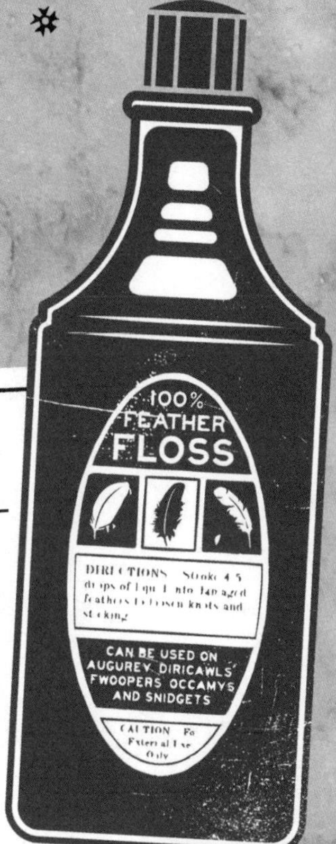

Name: _____

Colour: _____

How to apply: _____

What kind of creature would it be used on: _____

_____

How long does it last? _____

Any other information: _____

_____

_____

_____

_____

_____

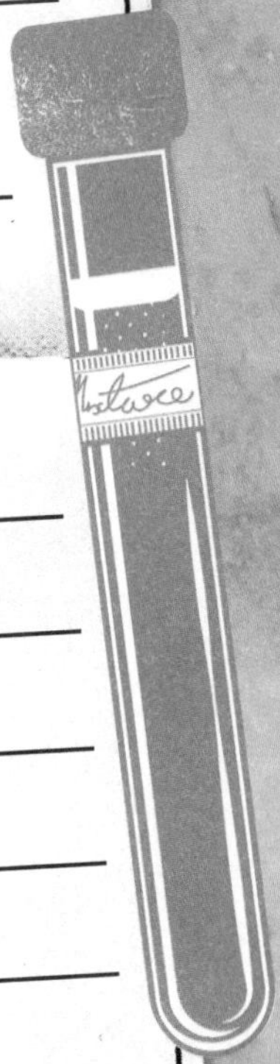

The Obscurus is defeated at the wands of a squadron of Aurors.

Newt uses "REVELIO!" to expose the Dark wizard.

Percival Graves' true identity as Gellert Grindelwald is revealed. He is defeated and led away to be imprisoned.

Frank the Thunderbird spreads Swooping Evil venom through a storm to Obliviate New York's No-Majs of the devastating event.

PEACE RESTORED

With the Obscurus destroyed and Grindelwald behind bars, New York City is a much more peaceful place. The characters can now move on with their lives, hoping that the worst is now behind them.

Newt can now safely allow Frank the Thunderbird to return to the desert plains of Arizona, while he sails back to England to work on his book.

Tina is recalled to serve as a MACUSA Auror. She shares a tearful goodbye with Newt.

Jacob is given a case full of rare silver Occamy eggshells by a kind stranger. He uses them to open his bakery.

Queenie reluctantly allows Jacob to have his memory wiped. She visits him at his newly opened pastry shop, even though he doesn't know who she is.

ENCHANTED DISPATCHES TO THE AMERICAN WIZARD

THE NEW YORK GHOST

MONDAY 6TH DECEMBER 1926

PRICE 0.03 DRAGOTS

HEADLINE NEWS

Find your finest quill! Imagine you had to write the lead story about recent events for *The New York Ghost*, the city's leading wizarding newspaper. What will your headline be?

RETURN TO LONDON

Having travelled the world, Newt returns to London and publishes his book. *Fantastic Beasts and Where to Find Them* makes Newt more famous than he ever wished to be.

When Grindelwald escapes and learns that Credence is alive, Dumbledore sets a mission for his former pupil.

Dumbledore tasks Newt with going to Paris and finding Credence before Grindelwald does. Dumbledore claims that Newt is the only one who can take on Grindelwald, and he himself cannot.

As Newt is unwilling to help the Ministry of Magic track down and destroy the Obscurus, his application for a travel permit is denied. Newt's plans to visit Tina in New York are dashed.

Complete your own permit to travel application.
Fill in all the details, then record your fingerprints.

MINISTRY OF MAGIC

APPLICATION NUMBER: ☐☐☐☐☐☐☐☐☐☐

NAME OF APPLICANT: _____

NATIONALITY: _____

REASON FOR TRAVEL: _____

PENDING

NAME OF APPLICANT: _____

NATIONALITY: _____

PRESENT ADDRESS: _____

DATE OF BIRTH: _____

PROFESSION OR OCCUPATION: _____

MINISTRY OF MAGIC ID NUMBER: ☐☐☐☐☐☐☐☐☐☐

STICK YOUR PHOTO HERE

PHOTO MUST BE RECENT.

1. R. THUMB	2. R. MERCURY	3. R. APOLLO	4. R. SATURN	5. R. JUPITER

HEIGHT: _____
WEIGHT: _____
COLOUR OF HAIR: _____
COLOUR OF EYES: _____
COMPLEXION: _____

GRINDELWALD'S ESCAPE

Gellert Grindelwald spent only a short time in prison for his crimes against MACUSA, before making his great escape. While Grindelwald remains at large, the wizarding world is a perilous place.

Grindelwald's carriage is pulled by Thestrals, winged horses that are visible only to those who have seen death.

The flight takes place on the roof of MACUSA Headquarters, as Grindelwald is being transferred to face trial in Europe.

Grindelwald is reunited with the Elder Wand, the most powerful wand in the wizarding world.

The villain's obsession with the Deathly Hallows continues, as Grindelwald seeks to increase his power.

Grindelwald's mission is to expose wizardkind in a move he believes would be for the greater good.

CIRCUS ARCANUS

When Credence finds his birth certificate, he discovers that his roots may lie in France. He joins a wizarding circus as a means of travelling to Europe.

The Maledictus is a circus performer who transforms into a creature. While her act may look spectacular, a blood curse dictates that one day she is destined to remain in her beast form forever.

Imagine you are travelling with a magical circus.
What would it be called? Which curious acts might perform?
Design a poster that will draw in the crowds.

LA PREMIÈRE FOIS EN FRANCE!

CIRQUE
ARCANUS

GRAND BOOK LAUNCH

Newt completes his book, *Fantastic Beasts and Where to Find Them*, shortly after returning to England from America.

The book is launched at wizarding bookshop, Flourish and Blotts, in Diagon Alley.

Imagine if Obscurus Books wanted to publish a book that you were writing. Which magical subject would you write about? Dream up a title and design the book's cover.

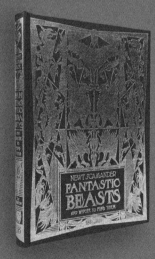

Newt's book would later appear on the required reading list at Hogwarts School of Witchcraft and Wizardry, where Newt himself once studied.

WHO IS LETA LESTRANGE?

Little is known about Leta Lestrange, the witch whose photograph Newt kept in his shed for years. The pair attended Hogwarts together, though lost touch after leaving school.

Leta and Newt developed a close friendship while at school, as both felt like outsiders.

Leta is now engaged to Newt's brother, Theseus Scamander.

A mysterious figure, Leta is troubled by a secret from her past.

Newt now carries a photograph of Tina with him.

Fashion of the 1920s was truly spellbinding! Leta's outfits have a
luxurious look.

Imagine you are designing your own 1920s clothes.
Sketch and colour them here.

POSTCARD FROM PARIS

Newt learns that Tina is in Paris when he reads a postcard, sent to Tina's sister, Queenie.

Imagine that you have travelled to Paris. Write a postcard about your trip. Who will you send your postcard to?

PORTKEY PASSAGE

Look around your room. Is there an object you could use as a Portkey? Draw it below.

A Portkey is an ordinary-looking object that will magically transport anyone who touches it to a particular destination.

The friends must first make their way to the White Cliffs of Dover to begin their journey.

Newt and Jacob arrive in Paris thanks to an old metal bucket!

NEW FRIENDS AND FOES

Newt comes across some unfamiliar faces in London and Paris and is reunited with people from his past. How many of these witches and wizards can you name? Draw a line to connect each name with the portrait.

ALBUS DUMBLEDORE

THESEUS SCAMANDER

THE MALEDICTUS

YUSUF KAMA

VINDA ROSIER

LETA LESTRANGE

BUNTY

SKENDER

Leta

Lestrange

Tina

Auror

Goldstein

THE POWER OF LOVE

Feelings run deep in the wizarding world – these magical matches were formed without the need to drink a powerful love potion! Which bonds do you think are the strongest? Rate your thoughts on these relationships by colouring in the feathers using the chart.

A fragile friendship
Sometime sweethearts
A magical bond
A perfect partnership
An eternal love

Tina and Newt were once oceans apart. Will they rekindle their relationship in the romantic city of Paris?

Relationships with No-Majs are forbidden for American witches and wizards. To what lengths will Queenie go to be with her true love, Jacob?

Newt and Leta were once close, though Leta later became engaged to Newt's elder brother, Theseus.

Credence and the Maledictus share a similar burden – a darkness inside them. Both outsiders, they find comfort in one another.

MAGICAL MINISTRIES

Each country has its own ministry that governs its magical community. Headquarters are often grand, usually with a concealed entrance to prevent raising suspicion among non-wizarding people.

MACUSA, USA

The Magical Congress of the United States of America is known as MACUSA for short. Its current headquarters are in New York City in the enormous Woolworth Building.

The congressional chamber is where MACUSA officials assemble to discuss matters of wizarding importance. President Seraphina Picquery leads the meetings.

MACUSA

APPLICATION FOR WAND PERMIT

HAVE YOU REMEMBERED?
Answer all questions.
Sign the application.
Insert your wand if asked to do so.
DO NOT FORGET to close this by using a SEALANT CHARM.

The Wand Permit Office is located in the basement. Any witch or wizard who wishes to use their wand while on American soil must first have been issued with a wand permit.

MINISTRY OF MAGIC, UK

The British Ministry of Magic (or MoM) can be found in London ... if you know where to look.

Newt's elder brother, Theseus Scamander, is Head of the Auror Office at the Ministry.

Leta Lestrange works at the Ministry alongside Torquil Travers, the Head of the Department of Magical Law Enforcement.

LE MINISTÈRE DES AFFAIRES MAGIQUES DE LA FRANCE

The French Ministry of Magic is situated in the French capital, Paris. With a glass-domed roof, it is the most stylish headquarters of the three countries.

Entry to the ministry is via a magical lift that appears from the roots of a tree.

The magical community in Europe is permitted a little more freedom than in the USA.

MAKING MAGIC

Used to channel the magical energies of a witch or wizard, wands are the most useful tools in the wizarding world. Even the most powerful wizards and witches possess a wand. Circle your favourite wand.

Newt Scamander

Gellert Grindelwald

Albus Dumbledore

Theseus Scamander

Tina Goldstein

Queenie Goldstein

Leta Lestrange

DESIGN YOUR OWN WAND

Decide which wood you'd like it to be made from, pick a material for the wand's core, then draw it in the box below.

Wood: *Core:*

☐ Alder   ☐ Cedar   ☐ Elder   ☐ Pine | ☐ Dragon heartstring   ☐ Thestral tail hair
☐ Beech   ☐ Dogwood   ☐ Hazel   ☐ Walnut | ☐ Phoenix feather   ☐ Troll whisker

LESSONS LEARNED

A gifted witch or wizard has an expert knowledge of spells and charms, to be used in times of trouble. Take a look at the following incantations – these are useful spells to have up your sleeve!

APPARE VESTIGIUM

Shows footprints and track marks

EXPELLIARMUS

Disarms an opponent's wand

NEBULUS

Conjures fog

PROTEGO DIABOLICA

Conjures a protective circle of fire

REPARO

Reassembles or fixes something that has been broken

VENTUS

Traps a person in a hurricane for one

UNWELCOME VISITORS

Torquil Travers leads a visit of Ministry Aurors to Hogwarts School of Witchcraft and Wizardry to interrogate Albus Dumbledore.

The Ministry wants Newt to help them track down Credence, they believe he is working under Dumbledore's orders.

Dumbledore is employed as the school's Defence Against the Dark Arts teacher.

Albus Dumbledore would later go on to become Hogwarts' finest ever headmaster.

Defence Against the Dark Arts is a compulsory subject for all years at Hogwarts. Dumbledore teaches his pupils how to keep themselves safe when faced with Dark magic.

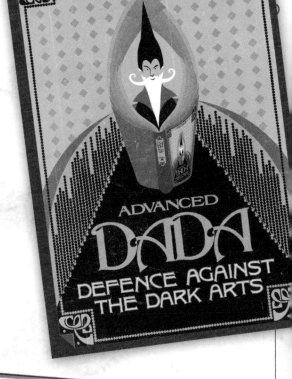

Topics include…
- **DEFENCE AGAINST MAGICAL CREATURES**
- **PROTECTION FROM DARK SPELLS**
- **DUELLING**

BEASTLY BOGGART

A Boggart is a shape-shifting creature that takes the form of the worst fear of the person who encounters it.

To defend against a Boggart, the Riddikulus spell is used, turning the Boggart into something amusing. Draw something scary dressed in funny clothes or in a situation that will make you laugh to banish the Boggart!

Newt was most frightened of being stuck in a desk job – his Boggart is a Ministry desk, which Newt transforms into a wooden dragon.

AN UNCERTAIN FUTURE

With the magical community deeply divided, many witches and wizards must decide whether to stand with the Ministry or join forces with Grindelwald. Which side do you think will come out on top?

Newt wishes to play no part in capturing Credence, though he would never support Grindelwald.

BRITISH MINISTRY OF MAGIC

- The Ministry wants to destroy the Obscurus once and for all, which would cause Credence's death.

- They wish to recapture and imprison Grindelwald before he grows more powerful still.

- Their policy is to keep the wizarding world secret from Muggles, in order to live peacefully.

GELLERT GRINDELWALD

- Grindelwald wants to expose the wizarding world to non-magical society, giving witches and witches more freedom, so that they no longer have to conceal their true nature.

- He secretly wants powerful wizards to rule over all non-magical beings.

- Grindelwald's army is growing, with rallies in Europe drawing support.

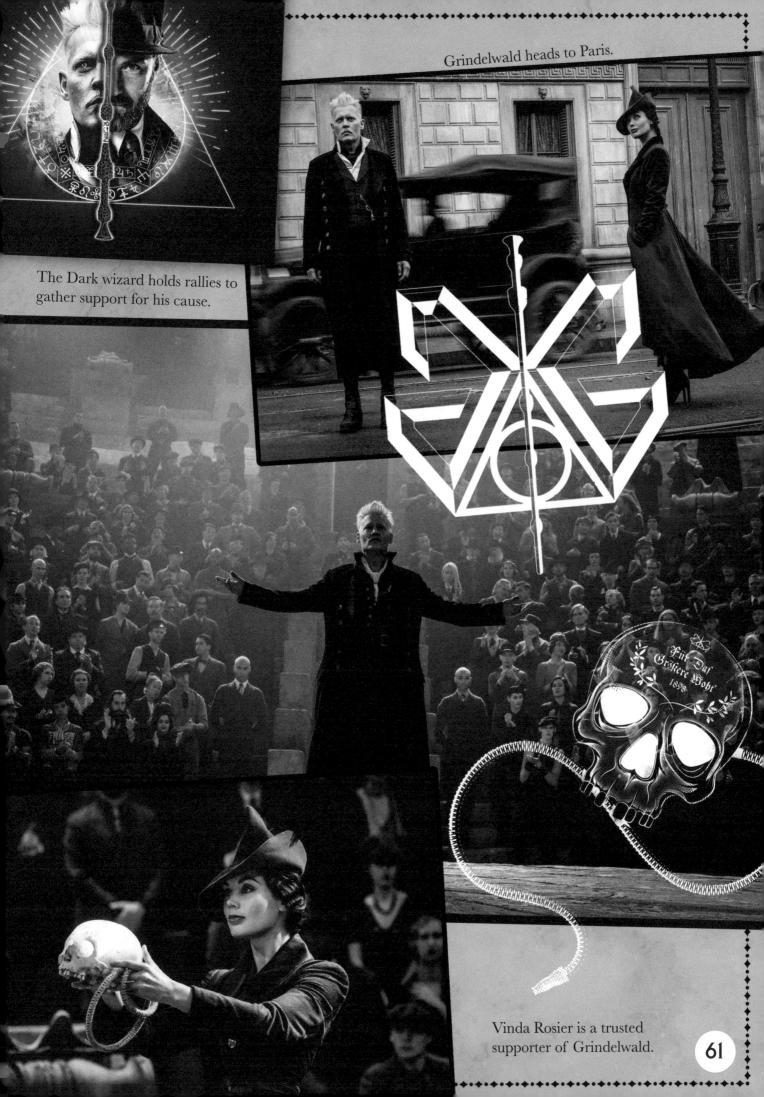

Grindelwald heads to Paris.

The Dark wizard holds rallies to gather support for his cause.

Vinda Rosier is a trusted supporter of Grindelwald.